¿Qué tal? Culture Resource Book

Blackline Masters

Guadalupe V. Lopez

Contributing Writer
Adam Sugerman

Program Authors
Ava Belisle-Chatterjee
Linda West Tibensky
Abraham Martínez-Cruz

National Textbook Company
a division of *NTC Publishing Group*

Project Director: Keith Fry
Project Managers: William Hrabrick, Frank Crane
Publishing Services International, Inc.
Art & Design Director: Karen Christoffersen
Design Manager: Linda Snow Shum
Cover Design: Linda Snow Shum
Page Design: Fulcrum Creative
Illustrators: Nancy Panacionne, Carolyn Gruber, Jon Pickard,
David Herrick, Mark Kellum

To the Teacher:
The blackline masters in this book are designed to be
photocopied for classroom use only.

Published by National Textbook Company,
a division of NTC Publishing Group

Printed in the United States of America.

CONTENTS

Cultural Activities Blackline Masters

Unidad 1

Masters 1–2: *Marionetas*

In Spanish-speaking countries, skilled artisans called *tallistas* carefully carve wooden *marionetas,* paint them, and outfit them in traditional fabric costumes and accessories.

Activity Type: Craft

Objective: Students make these traditional craft items out of cardboard, and then put on a puppet show.

Procedure: Help students use a ruler to transfer the *marioneta* pattern pieces onto posterboard.

Application: Have students describe their *marionetas*—arms, legs, body, and clothing. Encourage groups to put together a skit for a puppet show.

Master 3: *No Words Needed*

All over the world, people use their bodies to convey messages. A common gesture in one culture can mean something different in another.

Activity Type: Role-play

Objective: Students learn some forms and meanings of body language used in Spanish-speaking countries.

Procedure: Mime familiar gestures, such as "Okay," "Come here," and "No." Ask: "What body language would *you* use to give the messages shown here?" (For the first one, for example, students may nod in the direction of the person they're singling out.)

Application: Have students mime the new gestures. Encourage them to watch for these gestures on Spanish-language television or when they're with Spanish-speaking friends.

Unidad 2

Master 4: *¿Cuánto?*

People all over the world find ways to cut costs. In Latin America, many people practice the art of bargaining for *mercado* (market) items.

Activity Type: Role-play

Objective: Students learn a basic bargaining tactic for customers at a *mercado*.

Procedure: Ask students: "Do you know any places where it's OK to bargain for the best price?" (flea markets, used car lots, etc.) Have students bring in props and set up a *gorra* display where volunteers play seller and customer.

Application: Encourage students to visit a local *mercado* and observe bargaining tactics.

Master 5: *De paja o de lana*

Many of these hats are popular in the U.S.:

- The Panama hat got its name from gold-rush prospectors who bought the hats in Panama when returning from California.
- The Mexican *sombrero* served as a model for American cowboys' "ten-gallon" hats.
- The *chullo* has been keeping Peruvians warm for centuries. This cozy hat, with matching accessories, is a part of the winter line of major U.S. department stores.

Activity Type: Reading

Objective: Students learn about headwear from Spanish-speaking countries.

Procedure: Tell students that the title of the activity reads: "Of straw or of wool." Ask if they are familiar with any of the hats shown. If they have any of these hats at home, they can bring them in to show the class.

Application: If possible, display hats from Spanish-speaking countries around the room. Have students describe them.

Unidad 3

Master 6: *¡Qué pegue!*

Slang expressions are generally short-lived, especially with young people. The ones listed here, however, are part of the general public's vocabulary (like "cool" and "ain't" in American English).

Activity Type: Reading

Objective: Students learn and interpret common expressions used to describe people.

Procedure: Read and discuss the expressions one at a time. Ask if students know similar English expressions.

Application: Have students use these expressions to describe illustrations in the Student Book.

Master 7: *La Gigantona y El Cabezón*

These characters steal the show in the *carnaval* procession in Nicaragua. *La Gigantona,* with her floppy arms and outlandish make-up, entertains the crowd. She lumbers along the parade route to the beat of a huge drum, her arms whipping around at every turn. Her partner, *El Cabezón,* is about half her height. Someone, usually a child, maneuvers the oversize head from inside a wooden frame.

Activity Type: Craft/modeling

Objective: Students make sculptures to represent Nicaraguan carnival characters.

Procedure: Encourage students to paint *La Gigantona's* exaggerated features in bright colors. Show them how to gather the tissue paper to make the skirt.

Application: Vote on the best sculptures.

Unidad 4

Master 8: *El patio de mi casa*

This song takes many turns after players drop to the ground. Another version has the players scatter in a game of tag after singing:

> *Chocolate, molinillo* (a wooden whisk for whipping hot chocolate)
> *Corre, corre, que te pillo* (Run, or I'll nab you)
> *Estirar, estirar* (Stretch, stretch)
> *Que te voy a alcanzar* (I'm going to catch you)

Activity Type: Song/game

Objective: Students learn the importance of *el patio,* and then play a traditional game called *El patio de mi casa.*

Procedure: Go over the song, paying special attention to *agáchate* as the cue for everyone to drop down.

Application: Have students get into large groups, holding hands. Have them set the circle in motion as you cue the song.

Master 9: *Mi casa es tu casa*

Hospitality is a core value in Spanish-speaking countries, as these expressions show.

Activity Type: Reading

Objective: Students learn and interpret typical Latin American sayings about home.

Procedure: Prior to reading the Spanish sayings about home, have students share any from their own cultures ("Home sweet home"; "A man's home is his castle"; etc.).

Application: After reading the Spanish expressions, students can compare them with home-related expressions they know.

Cultural Activities

Unidad 5

Master 10: *La tabla huichola*

Tabla huichola is also known as "Mexican yarn painting." Popular subjects in this folk art include birds, the sun, and flowers.

Activity Type: Craft

Objective: Students create this traditional wall hanging.

Procedure: Before you begin, have students cut the scraps of yarn into pieces 2 inches to 12 inches long. Encourage students to be free with their color choices. Help them place the strands of yarn right next to each other so the posterboard doesn't show.

Application: Display the boards around the classroom. Vote on the most colorful *tabla,* most interesting design, etc.

Master 11: *Veo, veo*

As the game shows, the speech of Spanish-speaking children contains many "pint-sized" words—those ending in *-ito* and *-ita.*

Activity Type: Game

Objective: Students learn this traditional game, similar to "I Spy."

Procedure: Ask: "Why does this conversation say *cosita* instead of *cosa?"* Compare it to the difference between "dolly/doll" or "doggie/dog." Have students come up with other examples. Then, with a volunteer "spying" an object in the classroom, play a few rounds.

Application: Play this game using the home-related vocabulary from the Student Book unit.

Master 12: *Moorish Tiles*

The Moors, a Muslim people of Arab and Berber ancestry, ruled Spain from the eighth to the twelfth centuries. Since the religion of Islam forbids artistic rendering of living things, Moorish tiles feature abstract designs.

Activity Type: Craft

Objective: Students make models of typical Moorish tiles.

Procedure: Have students color these tile designs, or have them use graph paper to create their own.

As an extension, students can create actual Moorish-style tiles at home. Here's how:

With soap and water, wash a pre-glazed tile and let it dry. Coat with a layer of turpentine to create a tacky surface that accepts pencil marks. Draw or trace a design on the tile. Paint it with oil-based paints. Bake in a 350-degree oven for thirty minutes. Cool, then wash again to remove turpentine residue and pencil marks.

Application: Post cardboard tile designs around the room.

Unidad 6

Master 13: *Adivina en la cocina*

Activity Type: Riddles

The kitchen is the heart of the Hispanic home. Here children learn their first rhymes: verses which recount the lighthearted bickering of *la olla y el comal* (the pot and the griddle) and *adivinanzas* (riddles) such as these.

Objective: Students try to guess traditional riddles about kitchen items.

Procedure: Ask students if they recall a movie in which kitchen items come to life *(Beauty and the Beast).* Have them imagine the items shown here getting up, talking, and moving on their own.

Application: Have students draw the kitchen items with their *adivinanza* personalities: a busy broom with a chicken tail; a harried spoon diving into soup; a hungry table eyeing a meal.

Master 14: *Tía Zorra and the Fish*

This Venezuelan folktale is just one of many tales of crafty animals who play tricks on each other.

Activity Type: Reading

Objective: Students read a traditional folktale from Venezuela.

Procedure: Have students read the story and try to explain it in their own words. What is their opinion of *Tía Zorra*'s behavior?

Application: Have students create a different ending to the story—perhaps one where *Tía Zorra* is not so successful.

Master 15: *Menea la sopa*

This game is one of many versions of *sillas musicales* (musical chairs), except that this one is *sin música* (without music).

Activity Type: Game

Objective: Students play a traditional party game centered around the kitchen.

Procedure: Go through the "counting out" rhyme, line by line. Students will learn this vocabulary *(cuchara, tenedor, plato)* in Unidad 8. Write the phrase students will recite: *Menea la sopa, menea la sopa, para que quede sabrosa.* Remind students that the cook must tap the floor *three* times.

Application: Encourage students to play this game the next time they're at a party.

Unidad 7

Master 16: *Little Tortillas*

Children in Mexico and Central America probably remember someone in the family patting out *tortillas,* so the clapping motion in this song comes quite naturally to them.

Activity Type: Song

Objective: Students learn a *tortilla*-making song from Mexico.

Procedure: Sing the first verse of the song once or twice with the class. Then have the whole group practice the clapping part. Next have one group clap while the other sings.

Application: Have volunteers try singing and clapping at the same time. Challenge students to perform the song at an accelerated tempo.

Unidad 8

Master 17: *A Dominican Shake*

Morir soñando, a creamy drink reminiscent of an orange-flavored vanilla ice-cream bar, is the drink of choice on February 27, when the Dominican Embassy staff in Washington, D.C., raises glasses to commemorate Dominican Independence Day.

Activity Type: Recipe

Objective: Students make *Morir soñando,* a fruit drink from the Dominican Republic.

Procedure: Ask students if they know any curious names of desserts.

Application: Encourage students to try the recipe at home and vary the amount of ice and sugar.

Master 18: *A Mango Pop*

The mango, a native of India, is believed to have come to the Americas by way of Brazil.

Activity Type: Reading/recipe

Objective: Students set up a fruit stand with authentic presentation of a *mango.*

Procedure: Take precaution when spearing the *mango* with the sharp dowel. Have plenty of napkins on hand for this messy treat!

Application: Encourage students to prepare a *mango* like this for a special breakfast treat.

Cultural Activities

Master 19: *How the Ants Saved the Corn*

The Maya probably had the greatest of the ancient civilizations in Central America. Their empire included what is now Southern Mexico, Guatemala, Honduras, and El Salvador. It flourished from 300–900 A.D. Over forty Mayan languages are still spoken today.

How the Ants Saved the Corn is one of many Mayan legends that show the importance of corn.

Activity Type: Reading

Objective: Students read this Maya legend about a group of clever ants who save the corn crop.

Procedure: Tell students they are going to read a legend about corn. Then ask them to give their opinion of the different characters: birds, ants, gods, and people.

Application: Ask students if they know any similar stories or legends.

Unidad 9

Master 20: *Desayuno de papaya*

The *papaya,* also known as the pawpaw, has a different name in Cuba: *fruta bomba.* The *papaya* tree gives fruit all year round.

Activity Type: Reading/recipe

Objective: Students read about the *papaya* and its benefits, and then try it for breakfast.

Procedure: Bring in a large *papaya* and cut through it to expose the milky *papaína* for students to see. Then cut the fruit into small chunks for tasting with lime juice and salt. Have students rate the taste on a scale of one to ten, one ten being delicious.

Application: Encourage students to experiment with this fruit in other recipes.

Master 21: *Bate, bate, chocolate*

Chocolate caliente can be made with either milk or water. It is also mixed with spices to make *mole poblano* (a rich chocolate and chile sauce). The coarse-ground Mexican chocolate doesn't melt completely, so the drink should be served immediately after whipping.

Activity Type: Reading/recipe

Objective: Students learn the history of chocolate and make this typical breakfast beverage of Spain and Latin America.

Procedure: Bring in a large thermos full of *chocolate caliente* and have a "taste-test." If possible, bring in a *molinillo,* the special wooden whisk which is twirled between the hands to whip the chocolate. It is sold at Hispanic markets.

Application: Encourage students to treat their families to a pot of *chocolate caliente.*

Unidad 10

Master 22: *¿Comes o cenas?*

This ancient game from Mexico is similar to another one called *Los frijolitos* (little beans).

Activity Type: Game

Objective: Students play a traditional party game from Spanish-speaking countries.

Procedure: Have each student bring in twelve beans in a plastic sandwich bag.

Application: Challenge students to speak and react quickly while playing the game. You may want to give prizes to the quickest, most skillful players.

Master 23: *¡Buen provecho! (Have a Good Meal!)*

These sayings reveal traditional ideas about food and mealtimes in Spanish-speaking countries.

Activity Type: Role-play

Objective: Students practice typical expressions which highlight the value placed on mealtimes.

Procedure: Read the sayings one at a time; then ask students to interpret the meaning. Help students with the meaning of *Dame pan y llámame tonto,* said of someone who doesn't mind insults, as long as there is some material gain.

Application: Ask: "Do you think most people you know would agree with these sayings?"

Unidad 11

Master 24: *A (Latin American) Cowboy's Day*

Until 1900, the *gaucho*'s job was to take cattle to the markets in Buenos Aires, riding for weeks on end on the open plains of the *pampas*. Now he rides pick-up trucks and works as a hired hand on *estancias* (big ranches).

Activity Type: Reading

Objective: Students learn about the *gaucho*'s routine.

Procedure: Prepare students for the reading by providing a brief history of the *gaucho,* and telling how his daily routine has changed.

Application: Have students compare the *gaucho*'s routine with that of the American cowboy.

Master 25: *Clean and Natural*

People in Latin America use items found in nature to make all sorts of personal grooming aids which are often superior to commercial products.

Activity Type: Reading

Objective: Students learn about natural hygiene and personal grooming items from Latin America.

Procedure: If possible, bring in some of the items for students to see.
Application: Encourage students to try some of these items and report their experiences.

Unidad 12

Master 26: *Maestra querida*

Spanish-speaking countries celebrate *el Día del Maestro* on different days. It's April 13 in Ecuador and May 15 in Mexico. In some places, there are no classes that day. Teachers are showered with gifts, songs, and poems.

Activity Type: Reading

Objective: Students learn about the attitudes of Spanish-speakers toward teachers.

Procedure: Prepare students for the activity by asking them to think about favorite teachers they have had, and how they showed appreciation to these teachers.

Application: Encourage students to compare these Latin American attitudes with their own attitudes toward teachers.

Master 27: *Brinca la tablita*

Children the world over use songs and rhymes to remember school-related facts. *Brinca la tablita* is also challenging and fun as a game.

Activity Type: Game/song

Objective: Students play a traditional game which tests their coordination skills.

Procedure: Place a board 5 feet long and 8–12 inches wide on the floor. Have students line up on one side. Have those waiting their turn sing the song while the jumper concentrates on hopping over the board.

Application: Encourage students to use this song to hone their addition and Spanish skills at the same time.

Maps and Facts

The goal of the *Maps and Facts* section is to develop students' map reading skills, as well as to augment their knowledge of the geography and history of the different Spanish-speaking countries.

Each blackline master includes a few basic country facts (capital, independence day, population, and currency), a drawing of the country flag, a country map, and an inset map of the country in its respective region. The country maps indicate cities, important landmarks such as mountains (+) and rivers, and archaeological sites (Δ). Encourage students to use the *Maps and Facts* pages as a personal atlas which they can update as they learn more about each country.

The order of the seven countries that appear in this book is not meant to suggest any sequence of treatment. Further, how you use the *Maps and Facts* masters is a matter of personal choice. We have included, however, several suggestions for using the masters to involve students in learning more about each country.

1. Have students color the national flag. Its principal colors are indicated on the page.
2. Ask students to create cutout maps of each country to hold up as you ask different questions: What is the largest country? The smallest country? What country is bordered by rivers?
3. Play a name-the-capital game. Write on the chalkboard dashes to represent letters of a capital city (e.g., Caracas: _ _ _ _ _ _ _). Have students guess its name by asking you yes/no questions such as: *¿Está en Bolivia? ¿Está en el Caribe?*
4. Play a game with students using codes for geographical places. Develop a code (e.g., A = 1, B = 2, etc.) and have students decipher it. (Using the previously mentioned code, Sucre would be 19 – 21 – 3 – 18 – 5.)
5. Assign different countries to groups of students and instruct them to come up with facts to include on their masters—for example, the population of the capital city.
6. Make a history/geography word search or a crossword puzzle for students to solve.
7. Assign different countries to students and tell them to find where different products are grown or made and indicate this on the maps.
8. Have groups of students locate a country's internal political boundaries (e.g., autonomous regions, provinces, departments, states).
9. Ask students to research the location of the Aztec, Maya, and Inca empires.
10. Ask students to write a short biography of a famous person from an assigned country.

As you work with students on each map page, provide them with information about the country that you think is interesting or important. For example, for the countries covered in this book you may wish to share the following with students.

Uruguay:
Uruguay has an extensive river system. A dam on the Río Negro has created the largest artificial lake in South America (Embalse del Río Negro).

El Salvador:
El Salvador's northern border with Honduras is very mountainous. There are more than twenty active volcanoes in the north of the country.

Cuba:
José Martí was a writer and leader of the Cuban independence movement which culminated in the War of Independence (1895–1898). He is revered in Cuba just as Simón Bolívar is in other parts of Latin America.

Bolivia:
Bolivia is unique in Latin America in that it has two capitals. La Paz is the administrative capital, where most government offices are located. Sucre is the country's judicial capital and is the seat of the Bolivian Supreme Court.

Panamá:
Completed in 1914, the Panama Canal is one of the engineering wonders of the world. Almost a century after its opening, it continues to be a major artery for world commerce.

Venezuela:
Located in a remote area of southeast Venezuela, Angel Falls is the highest waterfall in the world (3,212 ft.). It was discovered by U.S. aviator James Angel in 1935.

Argentina:
Buenos Aires is the center of industrial, political, and cultural life in Argentina. Its metropolitan area has a population of 11,000,000. Because of its architecture, broad avenues, and beautiful parks, it is often compared to Paris.

MARIONETAS

Wood carvers in Spanish-speaking countries make wooden *marionetas* (stringed puppets). These puppets can be anybody: flamenco dancers from Spain, *gauchos* from Argentina, or tropical dancers with fruit on their hats.

Here's how to make your own *marioneta.* You need:

- Half of an 11 by 14-inch sheet of posterboard
- 12 brass paper fasteners
- 3 plastic curtain rings (1/2 inch in diameter)
- Thin cotton string
- Glue; construction paper; scissors; a ruler

Make drawings on posterboard and cut out the parts. Punch holes where you see circles in the pictures. Round off the corners. Put the *marioneta* together with paper fasteners.

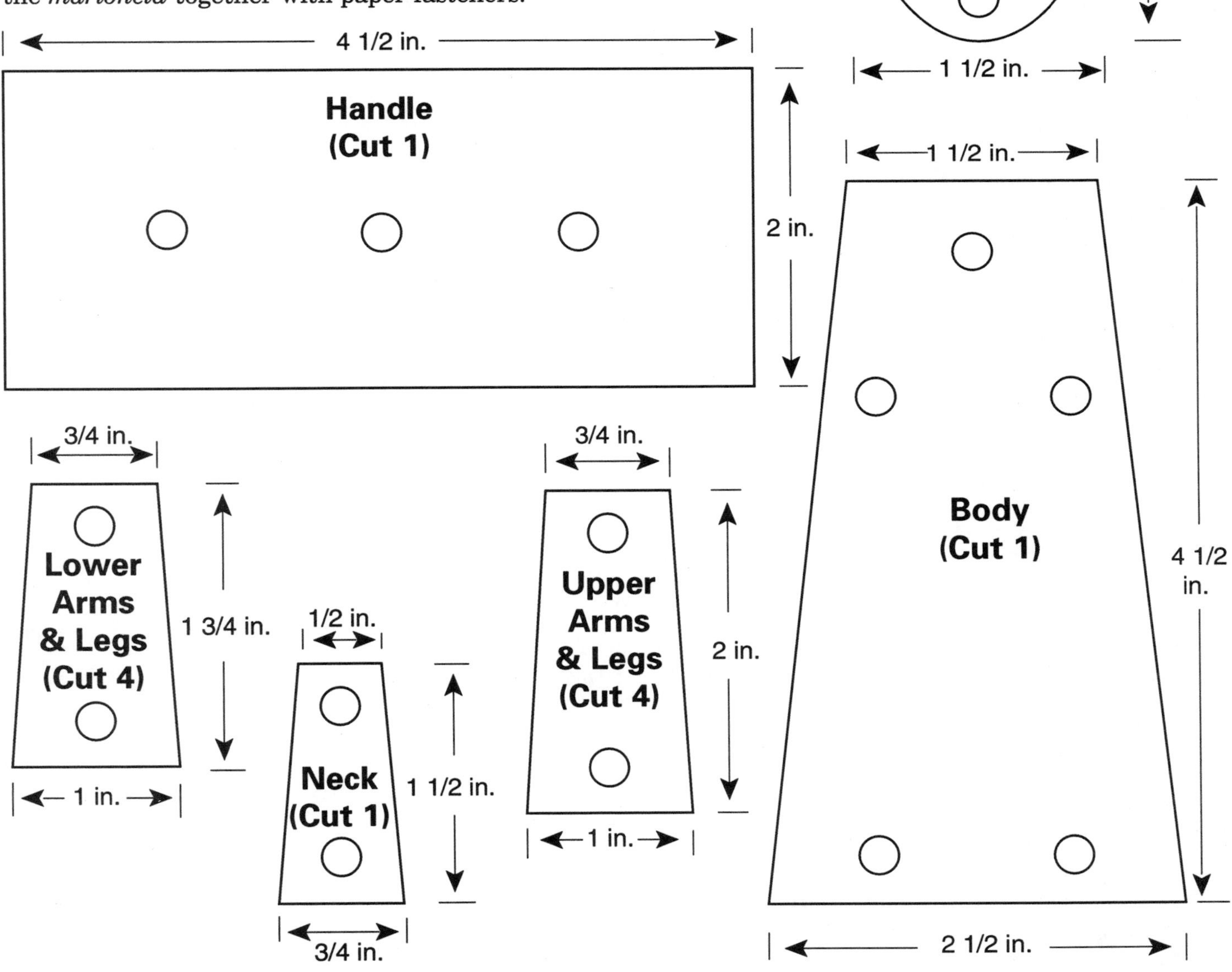

MARIONETAS, PAGE 2

1. Cut a piece of string 15 inches long. Tie one end to the hole at the top of the head. Slip the other end through the center hole in the handle, and tie it to a ring. The *marioneta* now hangs from the handle.

2. Cut two pieces of string 24 inches long. Tie one to the end of each arm, attaching it through the punched hole. Slip a brass fastener into the hole in each arm to weigh it down. Now you can fit each string to the handle.

3. Work with one arm string at a time. First slip the string through the hole in the handle. Then tie the end loosely to the ring. Lift the *marioneta* up by the handle and fix the string until the arm hangs comfortably. Tie the string to the ring.

Decorate your *marioneta*. Then have a puppet show!

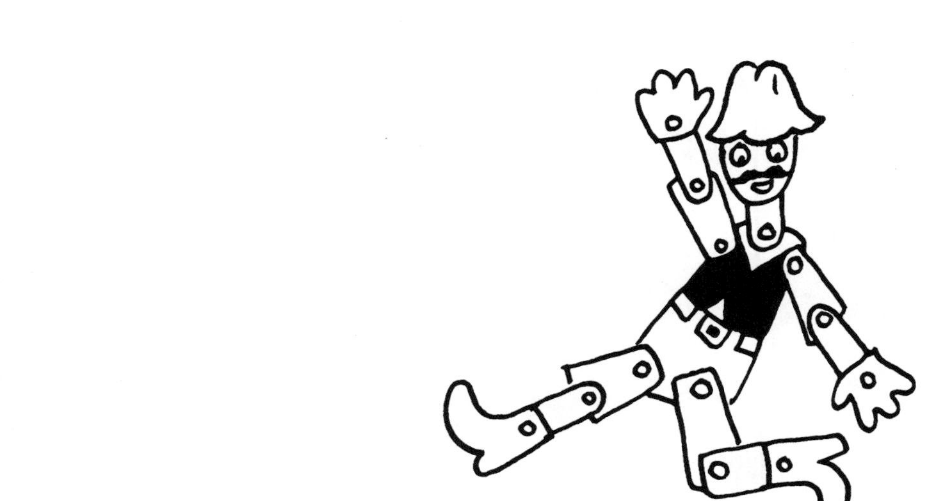

NO WORDS NEEDED

Can you talk without words? Sure you can! You might use a "thumbs up" to mean "Everything's okay," or a nod to mean "Yes." To see how people in Spanish-speaking countries do this, match pictures 1, 2, 3, with messages A, B, or C.

Pictures

1.

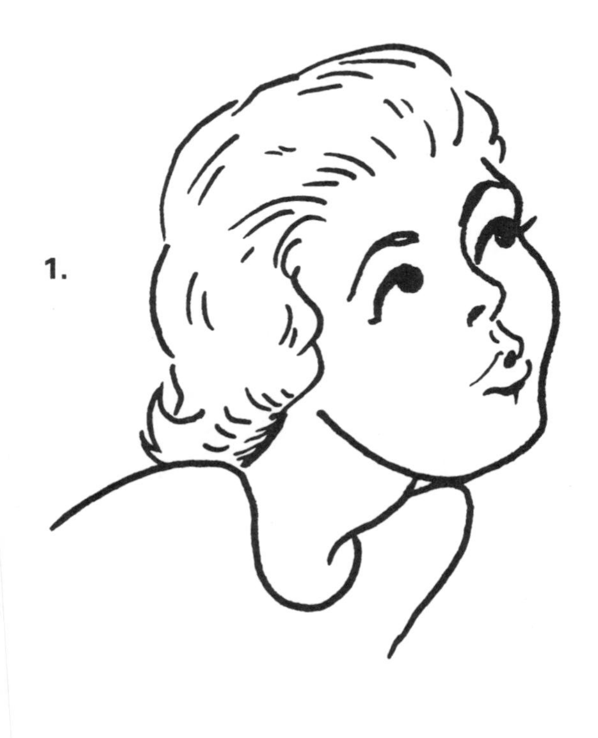

2.

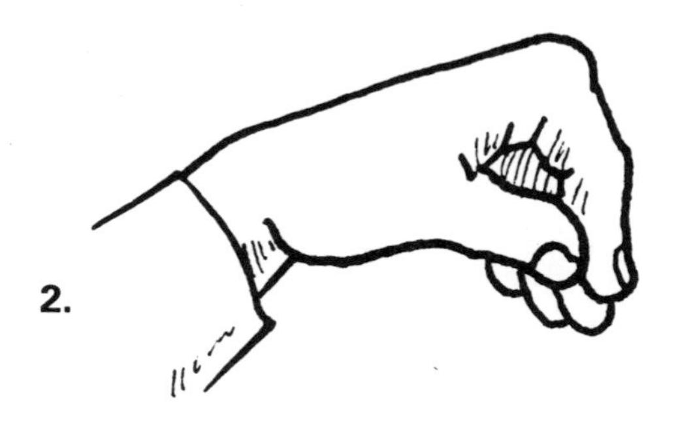

3.

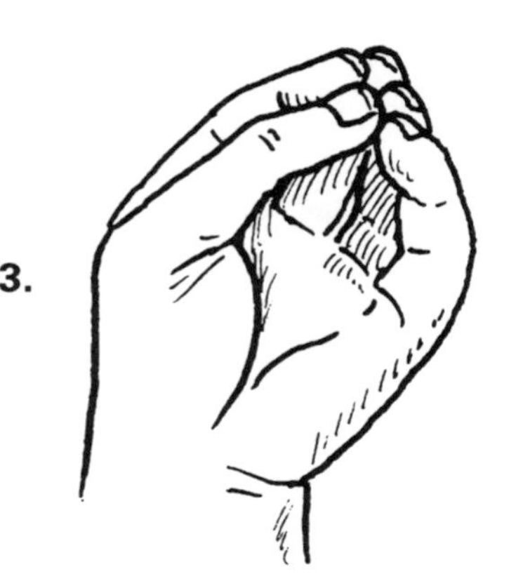

Messages

A. *¡Ven!* (Come here!) Picture Number _____

B. *¡Hay muchos, muchos estudiantes en la clase de español!* (There are many, many students in Spanish class!) Picture Number _____

C. *¿Quién es aquella maestra?* (Who's that teacher over there?)
Picture Number _____

For answers and more information, turn this page upside-down.

Answers

A: Picture Number 2. To call someone over, move all four fingers back and forth, palm down.

B: Picture Number 3. To say "a huge amount," touch the tips of all five fingers together, palm up.

C: Picture Number 1. To point, use lips instead of fingers.

So the next time you want to point, pucker up!

¿CUÁNTO?

Here's how to buy a cap at a *mercado.*

Say you're at a *mercado* in Quito, Ecuador. You see these great-looking baseball caps. You've got to have one—but don't let the seller know that!

1. Walk, don't run, to the table. Greet the seller.

2. Slowly pick up a cap and look it over. It's well made. It's your favorite color. Do you hand over the money now? No! Ask "How much?"

3. The seller's answer is "2,500 *sucres.*" Pretend to think it over. Turn the cap over a lot, then put it back.

4. Start to walk away slowly. Say "Thank you, sir. See you later."

5. The seller calls you back: "Wait! This cap's beautiful, and the color looks very good on you! Come on, buy it!" He holds the cap up. It *is* great, but don't give in yet.

6. Agree! Say "Yes, it's beautiful." Then say "But 2,500 *sucres?* I only have 2,000."

7. The seller thinks fast. He says "Okay, okay. 2,000 *sucres.*" Hand him the money.

8. (Now you can smile!)

DE PAJA O DE LANA

From palm leaves or velvet or threads,
Baseball blues or in fireman reds,
If you need a good prop,
You will find me on top,
In all cultures where people have heads!

Yes, it's hats! Read on to learn about special hats from Latin America:

Sombrero de panamá
This men's hat really comes from Ecuador and Colombia, not Panama. It's made by hand from the leaves of a plant called *toquilla. Toquilla* leaves look like palms.

Sombrero de jipijapa
In Colombia, people wear this palm hat when they're in the sun. It's like a big beach hat. Sometimes a hat will have two colors.

Sombrero de charro
Mexican cowboys wear this fancy hat made of felt. It may have sequins and a satin cord. The front of the brim slants down. The back slants up.

El chullo
In the Andean mountains, the weather is cold. This wool hat keeps people warm. It ties under the chin.

La paba
This Puerto Rican hat looks as if it has rays of sunshine around the brim. It's made of palm leaves that stick out, all the way around.

¡QUÉ PEGUE!

This expression means: "Everyone likes him—it's like he's covered with glue!" Here are some interesting expressions that kids in Spanish-speaking countries use to describe people. What do you think they mean?

¡Qué garruchón! (From Mexico. *Garrocha* means "pole").

Answer: A *garruchón* is a tall boy; a *garruchona* is a tall girl.

¡Está pegao! ("That person is sticky!" From the Dominican Republic. *Pegao* comes from *pegado,* "sticky.")

Es buena onda. ("He—or she—is a good wave." From Mexico.)

Answer: Both these sayings mean that someone is very popular. *Está pegá (from pegada)* is for a girl.

¡El uy uy uy! ("Mr. Can't Touch Me." In Mexico, little kids say *"¡Uy!"* when they see something dangerous, like a fire.)

Answer: *El uy uy uy* is a boy who is "super-cool"; a "super-cool" girl is *La uy uy uy.*

El super-pilas ("Mr. Super-charged batteries." From Ecuador.)

Answer: *El super-pilas* is a very clever, alert boy; *La super-pilas* is for a girl.

The next time someone calls you *super-pilas,* you'll know all that studying has paid off and no one can touch you! *¡Uy, uy, uy!*

LA GIGANTONA Y EL CABEZÓN

These two characters bounce along in Nicaraguan parades. *La Gigantona* is a giant woman with long yellow hair and crazy-colored clothes.

Her partner, *El Cabezón* ("Big Head") dances next to her. He's short, with a big head. It's so big, he can barely stand up straight.

Both these characters have wooden frames. People get inside the frames and move them around.

Make these parade characters yourself. (Smaller, of course!)

La Gigantona

You need a cardboard tube, yellow yarn, brown yarn, tissue paper, and markers.

1. Paint big eyes and mouth on the tube.
2. Make a braid out of yellow yarn. Staple it to her head.
3. Braid the brown yarn to make long arms. Staple them on.
4. Make a long tissue-paper skirt.

Make her arms sway back and forth!

El Cabezón

You need half a cardboard tube, a white balloon, felt, and markers.

1. Draw his face on the blown-up balloon.
2. Dress him in felt.
3. Tie a piece of yarn to the end of the balloon.
4. Put the yarn through the tube and pull it through a cut at the bottom.
5. Attach cardboard arms and feet to the tube.

Can he stand up, or is he too *cabezón?*

EL PATIO DE MI CASA

Most houses in Spain and Latin America don't have a backyard. *El patio* (the garden) is in the middle of the house. It has no roof, and people can enter it from different rooms. *El patio* might have a fountain, bird cages, and beautiful plants.

Kids in Spanish-speaking countries play *El patio de mi casa.* They hold hands in a circle. The circle moves as they sing:

El patio de mi casa	The patio of my house
Es particular:	Is very particular:
Cuando llueve se moja	When it rains, it gets wet
Como los demás.	Just like all the other ones.
Agáchate y vuélvete a agachar.	Bend over and bend over again.

Now everyone drops to the ground. Then they get back up and sing:

Las agachaditas	Those bent over
No saben bailar.	Don't know how to dance.

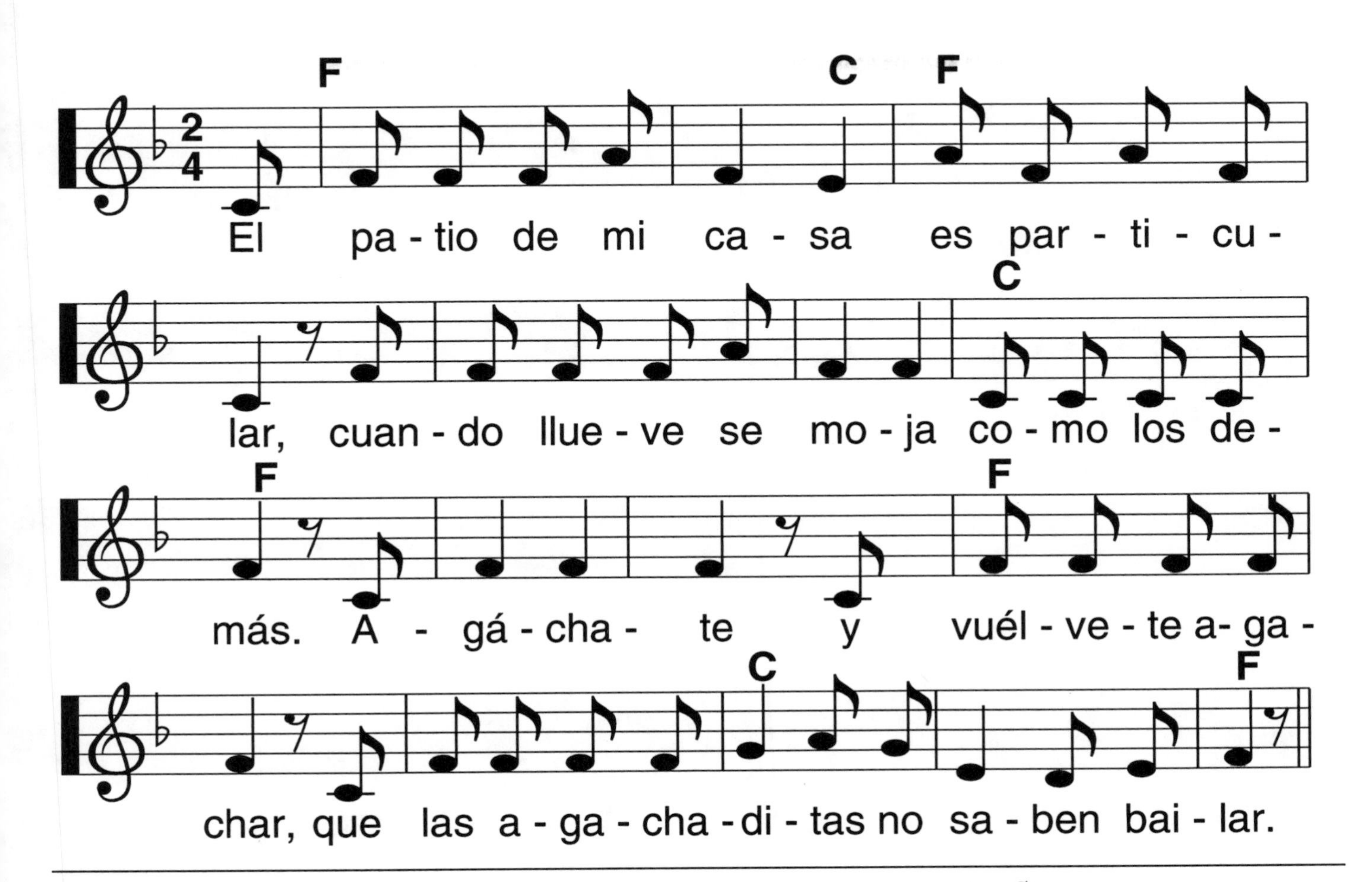

MI CASA ES TU CASA

In Spanish-speaking countries, that's a way to say "You're always welcome here!" People may give their address like this: *Madero 123; ahí está tu casa* ("Madero 123; your house is there"). When they talk about their house, they might say something like: *La escuela está al lado de mi casa, que es tuya también* ("The school's next door to my house, which is also yours").

Here are some other "house" expressions. What do they mean?

Amigo/Amiga de la casa
(friend of the house)

Answer: a friend of the family

Ofrecer la casa
(to offer the house)

People say: *Ofrecemos nuestra casa nueva. La dirección es . . .* It means "We offer our new house. The address is . . ."

Answer: to announce your new address

Echar la casa por la ventana
(to throw the house out the window)

Answer: to have a big party or celebration

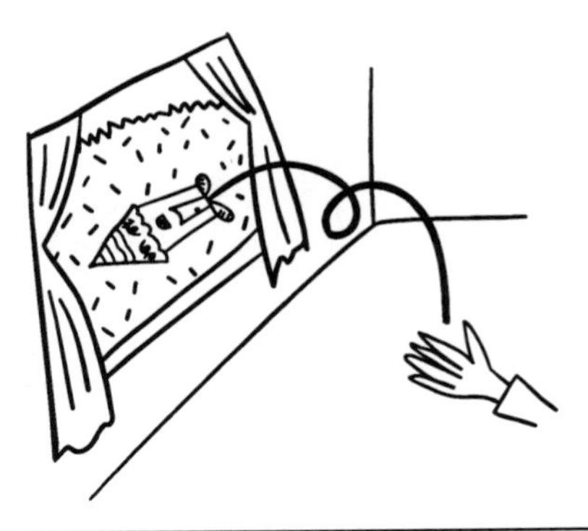

LA TABLA HUICHOLA

La tabla huichola (the name comes from the Huichol Indians of Mexico) is a "painting" with little pieces of yarn. You glue them to paper to make a design.

To make a *tabla huichola,* you need

Scraps of yarn
A wooden picture frame
A piece of colored posterboard
Glue; a small paintbrush; a paper cup

Cut the posterboard to fit the frame. Use a pencil and ruler to draw a 1-inch border. (Your *tabla huichola* shouldn't go beyond this border.) Draw a design like this one, or make your own. Mark your colors on the design ahead of time, or decide as you go along.

Pour some glue into the paper cup and mix in a few drops of water. Brush glue onto the paper. Attach the yarn. (It's a good idea to glue from the middle of your design. Do the outside parts last.) Cover the whole paper with yarn.

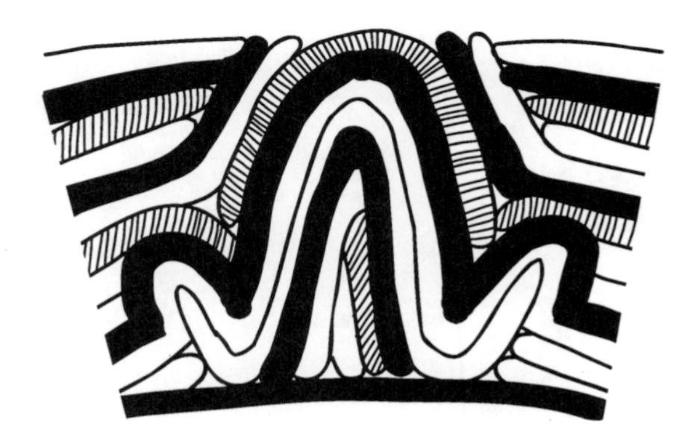

Let the glue dry. Then put the whole painting in the frame. A *tabla huichola* makes a great gift!

VEO, VEO

Kids in Spanish-speaking countries play this game. It's like "I Spy." Someone notices something in the room and calls out:

CALLER:	*Veo, veo.*	I see, I see.
GROUP:	*¿Qué ves?*	What do you see?
CALLER:	*Una cosita.*	A little thing.
GROUP:	*¿Y qué cosita es?*	And what little thing is it?
CALLER:	*Empieza con la . . .*	It starts with . . . (The caller says the first letter of the name.)
GROUP:	*¿Qué será? ¿Qué será?*	What can it be? What can it be?

Everyone tries to guess what it is. The person who guesses is the next caller. Next time you're in the living room with your family, play *Veo, veo!*

MOORISH TILES

The Moors ruled Spain for more than 400 years. They came from northwest Africa. They taught the Spanish people many things—even how to make beautiful tiles.

In Spain, you see Moorish tiles in patios, fountains, walls, and floors. They have designs like the ones on this page. The real tiles are clay, but you can make one out of cardboard.

Copy one of these designs (or one of your own) onto cardboard. Color it with fine-tipped markers or paints. A great color for these tiles is a deep, dark blue. It's called "Muslim blue."

Cut out your tile and glue it onto heavy cardboard.

Adivina en la cocina

Imagine your kitchen coming to life! Spanish-speaking kids do—they learn songs and sayings about *el comal y la olla* (a talking griddle and pot). And they learn riddles like these. Can you figure them out?

Paso por la sala. *Voy a la cocina.* *Muevo la cola* *Como una gallina.*	I pass through the living room. I go to the kitchen. I move my tail Like a chicken.

Answer: *la escoba* (the broom)

Subo llena y bajo vacía *Si no me apuro,* *La sopa se enfría.*	I go up full and come down empty. If I don't hurry, The soup gets cold.

Answer: *la cuchara* (the spoon)

Tengo patas pero no me puedo mover. *Llevo encima la comida,* *Pero no la puedo comer.*	I have legs, but I can't move. I carry the food, But I can't eat it.

Answer: *la mesa* (the table)

TÍA ZORRA AND THE FISH

This folktale from Venezuela tells what happens when *Tía Zorra* (Aunt Fox) and *Tío Zorro* (Uncle Fox) invite *Tío Tigre* (Uncle Tiger) to dinner.

One day, in the river by the forest, *Tío Zorro* caught three big fish. *Tía Zorra* was very pleased. They decided to invite *Tío Tigre* for a fish dinner. So *Tío Zorro* went out to look for *Tío Tigre.*

Tía Zorra started to fry the fish. "Mmm, these fish smell good," she thought. "I'm going to taste one." She did: it was delicious! In a few seconds, she ate it all. Then she tasted another fish. Pretty soon, she finished that one, too. "Oh, dear," she said. "I may as well eat the last one." And she did.

A few minutes later, *Tío Tigre* and *Tío Zorro* came in. *Tía Zorra* said: "The fish are still in the frying pan, keeping warm." "I'll set the table," said *Tío Zorro.* "We're very hungry—right, *Tío Tigre?" Tío Tigre* agreed. A wonderful fish smell was coming from the kitchen.

Tía Zorra showed *Tío Tigre* to the table. She whispered to *Tío Zorro:* "The fish are very tough. Go to the patio and sharpen three knives." *Tío Zorro* ran to the *patio* and began to sharpen the knives. *Tía Zorra* and *Tío Tigre* could hear the sound in the dining room.

Tía Zorra looked at *Tío Tigre.* "Do you hear that? *Tío Zorro*'s gone crazy! He wants to eat your ears! Run!" *Tío Tigre* was very frightened. He ran out of the house as fast as he could.

Tía Zorra yelled: *"Tío Zorro!* Hurry up—*Tío Tigre*'s running away with the fish!" *Tío Zorro* ran out the door, knife in hand. *"Tío Tigre!"* he yelled. "Let me have just one!" But *Tío Tigre* ran even faster. In fact, he was never seen again.

MENEA LA SOPA

Kids in Latin America play this game. It's like musical chairs, except that the chairs are in a circle. In the middle of the circle is a cook (*el cocinero* if it's a boy, *la cocinera* if it's a girl) pretending to stir a pot of soup with a yardstick. The other kids walk around the cook, saying *Menea la sopa, menea la sopa, para que quede sabrosa.* ("Stir the soup, stir the soup, so that it comes out tasty.") When the cook taps the floor three times with the yardstick, everyone (including the cook!) has to run for a chair.

Listen carefully: *el cocinero* might try to trick everyone and tap only once or twice. The person left standing is the next *cocinero.*

To choose your first *cocinero* or *cocinera,* use this "counting out" rhyme from Puerto Rico:

Yo tiro la cuchara,	I throw down the spoon,
Yo tiro el tenedor,	I throw down the fork,
Yo tiro cuatro platos,	I throw down four plates,
¡Y me voy a Nueva York!	And I'm off to New York!

LITTLE TORTILLAS

Do you sing or whistle while you're doing chores? Kids in Latin America sometimes sing this song while making *tortillas:*

Tortillitas de pan y de vino	Little tortillas of bread and wine
Para papá que viene en camino.	For daddy who's on his way home.
Tortillitas de pan y de queso	Little tortillas of bread and cheese
Para papá que va de regreso.	For daddy who's on his way back.

The song goes like this:

There's a clapping part that goes like this:

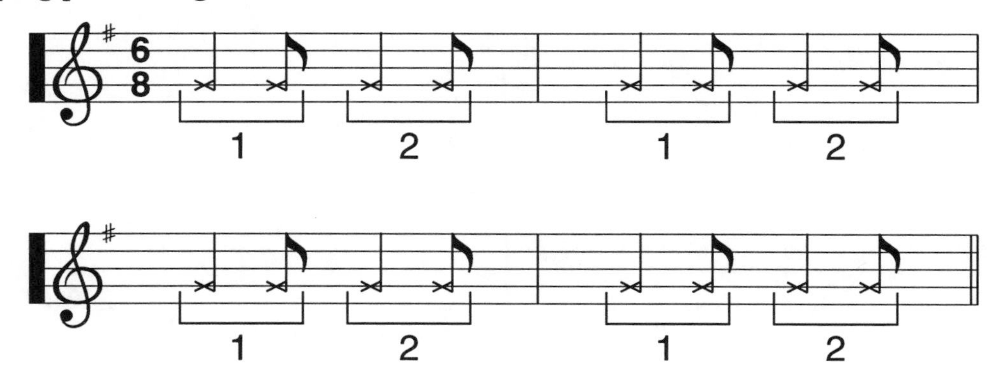

Clap your hands quickly, changing the hand that's on top with each clap.

Can you pat out perfect little *tortillas* while you sing?

A DOMINICAN SHAKE

In the Dominican Republic, people drink an orange-flavored milk shake called *morir soñando* (to die dreaming). It's an unusual name for a delicious drink!

Morir soñando

1 cup of ice
8 oz. evaporated milk
4 oz. freshly squeezed orange juice
1 teaspoon vanilla extract
1-2 tablespoons sugar

Put the ice and milk in the blender. Blend until smooth. Slowly add the orange juice, vanilla extract, and sugar. Pour into 2 tall glasses.

Serves 2

A MANGO POP

A favorite snack in Latin America is a huge, sloppy, fresh *mango* lollipop: a *mango* on a stick! They sell them this way in *puestos de frutas* (fruit stands).

On a hot day, a *puesto de frutas* is like cool water in the desert. People take a break and sit on a bench in the plaza to enjoy a sweet fruit treat. You pick a *mango,* and the seller prepares it. He puts it on a pointed wooden stick. Then he peels it, cuts it like a tulip, and adds spices.

Make a *mango* lollipop! You need:

Mangos
Limes
Salt
Chili powder (optional)
Wooden dowels (Have an adult sharpen each one like a pencil.)
Napkins

Prepare the *mango:*

Have an adult stick the dowel through the bottom of the *mango* to make a handle. Peel the *mango.* Make four cuts down the side of the *mango* to make a tulip shape. Sprinkle with lime juice, salt, and chili powder if you want.

HOW THE ANTS SAVED THE CORN

This Mayan legend tells how people almost lost their corn crop forever.

Once upon a time, the gods were angry with the people, so they hid the corn inside a huge rock. The hungry people searched and searched. The birds missed the corn, too.

One day the birds found the corn. But it was inside the rock. They tapped and pecked and hit the rock, but they couldn't get at the corn. Just then an ant came by, and a hungry bird tried to eat it.

"Don't eat me," said the ant. "I can get the corn."

"You?" said the bird. "You're just a little ant. If we can't break the rock, how can you?"

"Just wait," said the ant."Tomorrow you'll have your corn." So the birds agreed to wait.

The next day, there was a big pile of corn by the rock. A wind began to scatter the seeds.
The gods came to the rock. They asked the ant: "How did you get into the rock?"

"It was easy," said the ant. "My ant friends and I came to the rock at night. The moon lit up all kinds of holes that no one else could see. We went into the holes and brought out the corn, piece by piece. There were a lot of us, so it didn't take long."

The gods were angry. "You ruined our plans," they said. "We'll fix you and your ant friends." The gods tied threads to the anthill. They tied up every ant with a tight thread around the waist.

But the ants were smart. They chewed through the threads and ran away. Yet even now, ants have narrow waists from those threads.

When the people heard the ants' story, they thanked them. Even the birds were nice to them!

DESAYUNO DE PAPAYA

Latin Americans love *papaya* in the morning. On their way to school, kids might buy a slice of fresh *papaya* from a street seller and eat it on the playground.

The *papaya* is a big fruit: just one is enough for about ten people.

If you cut the rind of a green *papaya,* a milky liquid comes out. That's why people in Venezuela call it *lechosa* (milky). This liquid (and the rest of the plant) has something called *papaína.* People use *papaína* in medicines. It's also a softener. To make meat tender, chefs wrap it in *papaya* leaves.

Papaya is good for you, and it tastes great. Try some with blueberries for breakfast. Mix in a little vanilla yogurt, and maybe some chopped nuts or cereal. You'll feel great all morning!

Bate, bate, chocolate

El chocolate excelente,
Para poderse beber,
Tres cosas ha de ser:
Espeso, dulce y caliente.

—A Mexican saying

Excellent chocolate,
To be ready to drink,
Has to be three things:
Thick, sweet, and hot.

If you like chocolate, thank the Aztecs. They made a thick, rich drink called *tchocolatl.* It was made of *cacao, chiles* (hot peppers), and vegetables. The Emperor Montezuma used to drink it in cups of pure gold.

The Spanish came along and changed the recipe. Soon everyone in Europe was enjoying this rich, sweet drink. In Spain, *chocolaterías* serve *chocolate caliente* all the time.

In Mexico, people grind roasted *cacao* beans to make their *chocolate caliente.* Then they add cinnamon, almonds, and sugar. They whip the chocolate with a wooden whisk called a *molinillo.*

Chocolate caliente has changed a lot since the time of the Aztecs, but it's still a delicious drink. Try it for breakfast with crusty bread.

Chocolate caliente

1 tablet of Mexican hot chocolate
4 cups of milk

Place the milk and chocolate tablet in a heavy saucepan over low heat. Stir with a wire whisk until the tablet dissolves and the milk is hot, but not boiling. Serves 4.

¿Comes o cenas?

Kids in Latin America play this game at parties. It's like "Rock, Paper, Scissors." Everyone starts out with 12 dried beans.

Let's say David is Player 1. He hides some beans in his hand. Then he puts his hand out to Julia (Player 2).

PLAYER 1: *¿Comes o cenas?*(Do you eat lunch or dinner?)
PLAYER 2: *A manos llenas.* (By the handfuls.)
PLAYER 1: *¿Cuánto?* (How many?)

How many beans is David holding? Julia guesses three:

PLAYER 2: *Tres.* (Three.)

But David has seven beans. So he says:

PLAYER 1: *Tengo siete. Tres más cuatro son siete. Dame cuatro.* (I have seven. Three plus four is seven. Give me four.)

So Julia has to give up four of her beans.

What if Julia said ten beans instead of three? David would say:

PLAYER 1: *Diez menos siete son tres. Dame tres.* (Ten minus seven is three. Give me three.)

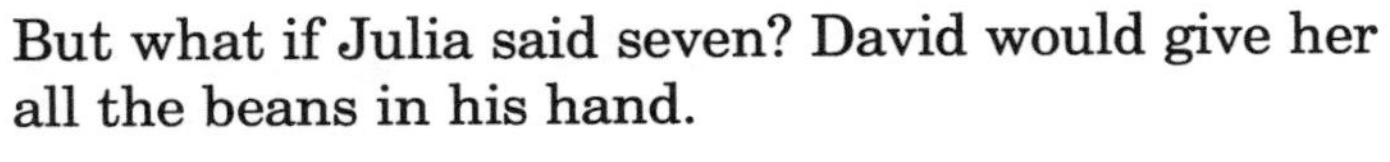

But what if Julia said seven? David would give her all the beans in his hand.

Pretty tricky, huh? Play *¿Comes o cenas?* with a partner. At the end of the game, the player with the most beans wins.

¡Buen provecho! (Have a Good Meal!)

Are meals important to you? Do you mind people talking while you're eating? Do you think about food a lot?

Look at these sayings from Spanish-speaking countries. What do you think they mean?

Barriga llena, corazón contento.	Full belly, happy heart.
Con buena hambre, no hay mal pan.	With real hunger, there's no bad bread.
Dame pan y llámame tonto.	Give me bread and call me foolish.
Yo soy como Orozco: *cuando como, no conozco.*	I'm like Orozco [a last name]: when I'm eating, I don't know you.
Estómago hambriento no tiene oídos.	A hungry stomach has no ears.

You've probably guessed it. In Spanish-speaking countries, meals are very important. People take time to enjoy their meals. Do you?

A (LATIN AMERICAN) COWBOY'S DAY

Here's a day in the life of a *gaucho* (cowboy) in Argentina.

Gaucho: San Antonio de Areco, Argentina

¡Hola! Me llamo Andrés Schuster. Soy gaucho. Yo me levanto a las cinco de la mañana. Me pongo mis bombachas, botas, corbata bola, cinturón de plata, y mi sombrero. Desayuno un vaso de leche con pan. Luego voy a trabajar. Yo cuido el ganado de la estancia del Sr. O'Higgins, en las pampas de Buenos Aires. Por la tarde, me reuno con los otros gauchos a tomar yerba mate. Luego seguimos trabajando. Después de trabajar, a veces hacemos un asado y cantamos canciones.

Hello! My name is Andrés Schuster. I'm a *gaucho.* I get up at 5:00 A.M. I put on my *bombachas* (baggy pants), *botas* (cowboy boots), *corbata bola* (string tie), *cinturón de plata* (silver belt), and *sombrero* (hat). I have milk and bread for breakfast. Then I go to work. I tend cattle on Mr. O'Higgins's ranch on the *pampas* (plains) of Buenos Aires. During the afternoon break, I get together with the other *gauchos* and drink *yerba mate* (a strong, hot tea). Then we get back to work. After work, we sometimes have a barbecue and sing songs.

Clean and Natural

To stay clean and well-groomed, many people in Latin America don't look much farther than the front door. Here are some natural cleaners that are better than most soaps:

Estropajo (scrubber)
This is like a sponge. It's made of *esparto,* a grass used to make rope. The *estropajo* makes the skin feel tingly as it rubs away dead skin.

Jabón de coco (coconut soap)
People heat chunks of coconut meat to extract the oil. Then they mix the oil with ashes to make soap.

Aceite de aguacate (avocado oil)
People make avocado oil like this:

Leave an avocado in the sun a few days. Wait for it to turn black. Strain the pulp through a cheesecloth. You'll get a soft, clear oil. People use this oil in their hair to make it soft and shiny. They also use it to make fine soaps.

MAESTRA QUERIDA

Read the statements. Who are they about?

You include me in after-school activities.
May 15 is my special day.
My name also means "master."
I get a lot of respect.

Surprise! They all refer to teachers in Latin America. Students there include a favorite teacher in after-school activities. They might invite their teacher for a bite to eat or to play a game of *fútbol* (soccer). (Some Latin American teachers aren't much older than their students. They can be as young as 19!)

May 15 is *el Día del Maestro* (Teacher's Day) in many Latin American countries. Kids sing songs and recite poems to their teachers on this day. *Maestro* also means "master"—someone who knows a subject very well, or teaches something very valuable.

Teachers in Latin America get a lot of respect. Kids like to spend time with them. People greet a teacher on the street with *¡Hola, maestra!* or *¡Hola, maestro!* (Hello, teacher!). It's a title of respect, like "ma'am" or "sir."

BRINCA LA TABLITA

Can you speak Spanish and do math at the same time? How about speak Spanish, do math, and hop over a board? Here's your chance to find out!

Try this playground game from Latin America. To play, place a long board on the floor. Take turns hopping from one side of the board to the other. When you get to the other side of the board, jump and turn in the air, landing on one foot. You should be facing in the opposite direction you started from.

Now here's the hard part. While you're doing all that, sing this song:

Brinca la tablita	Jump over the board
Que yo la brinqué.	I already jumped it.
Bríncala tú ahora—	Now you jump—
Que yo me cansé.	I'm already tired.
Dos y dos son cuatro,	Two and two are four,
Cuatro y dos son seis.	Four and two are six.
Seis y dos son ocho,	Six and two are eight,
Y ocho dieciséis,	And eight are sixteen,
Y ocho veinticuatro,	And eight are twenty-four,
Y ocho treinta y dos,	And eight are thirty-two,
Y diez que le sumo	And ten more that I add
Son cuarenta y dos.	Make forty-two.

MAPS AND FACTS

URUGUAY

Capital: Montevideo

Día de Independencia: 25 de agosto

Habitantes: 3,200,000

Moneda: nuevo peso

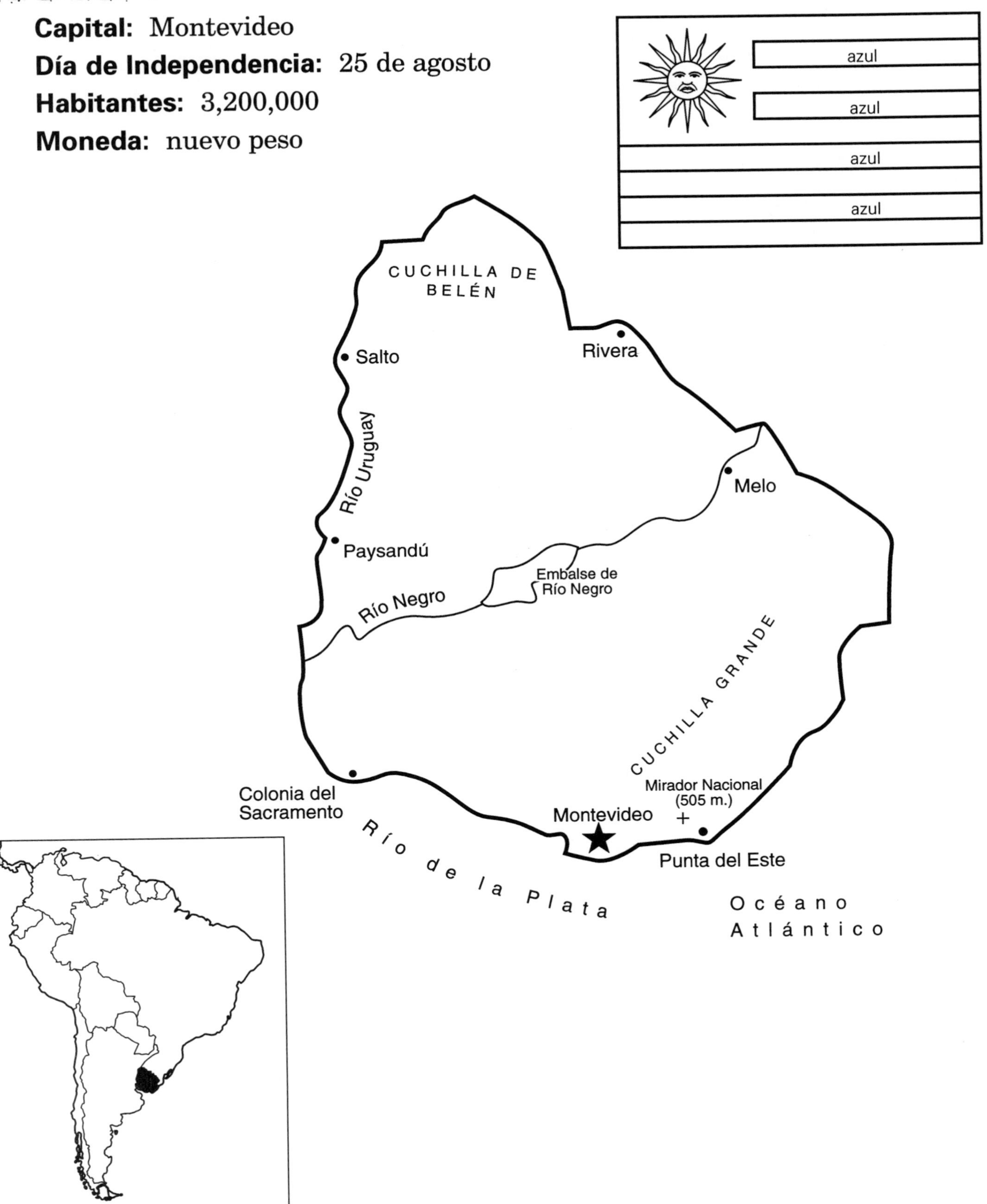

EL SALVADOR

Capital: San Salvador
Día de Independencia: 15 de septiembre
Habitantes: 5,900,000
Moneda: colón

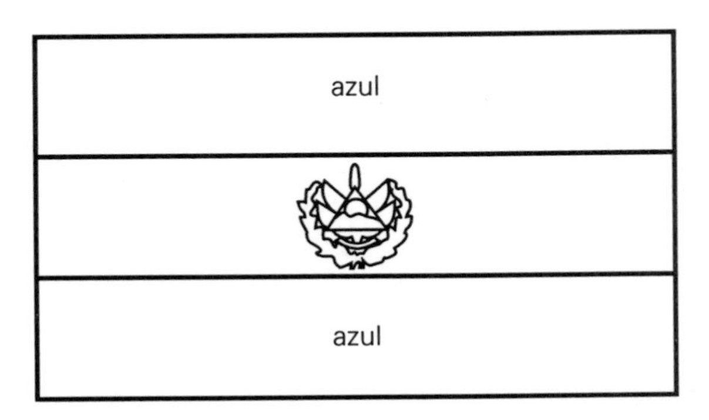

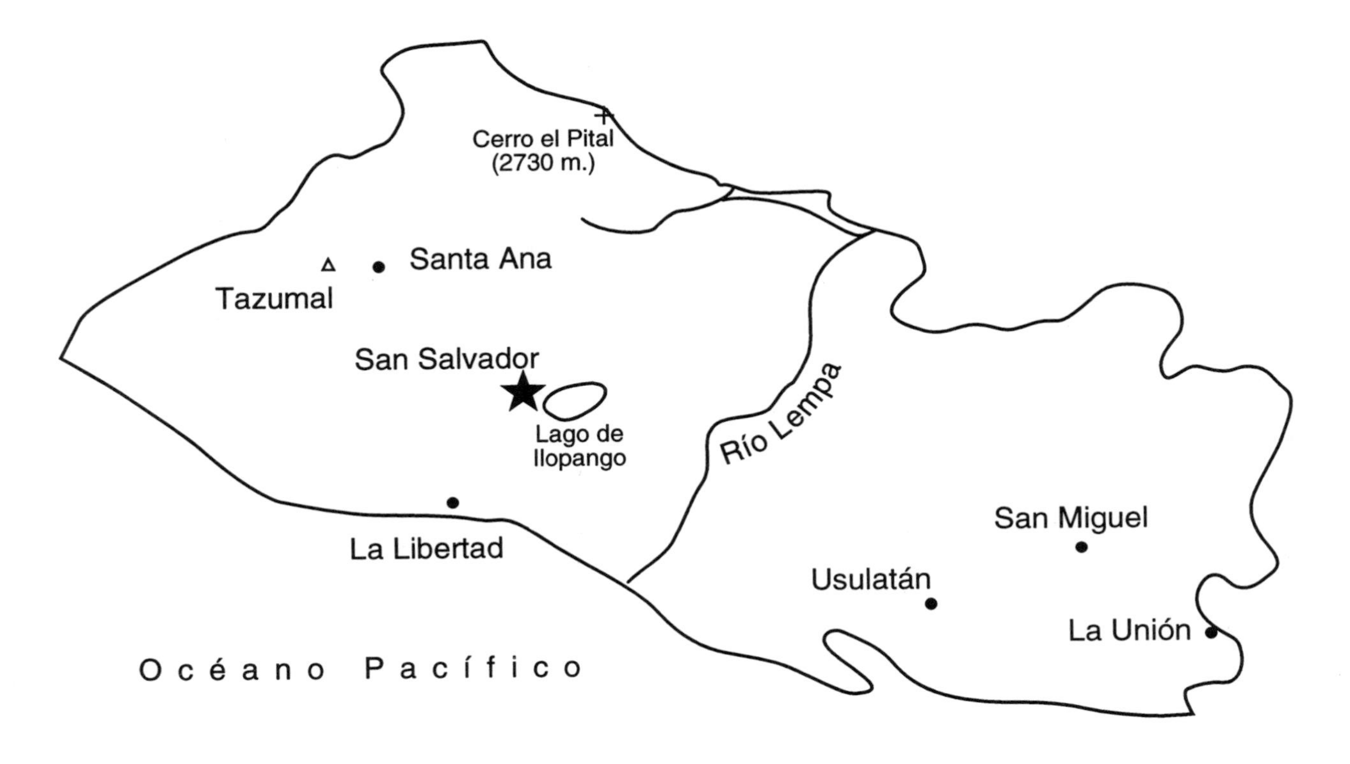

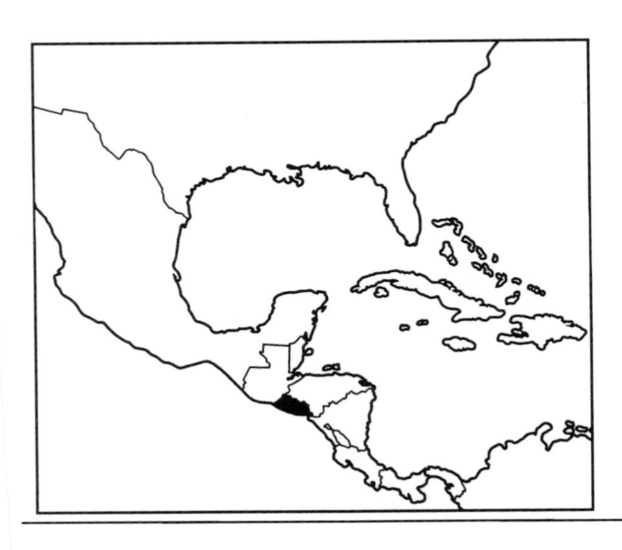

CUBA

Capital: La Habana
Día de Independencia: 20 de mayo
Día de la Revolución: 26 de julio
Habitantes: 10,900,000
Moneda: peso

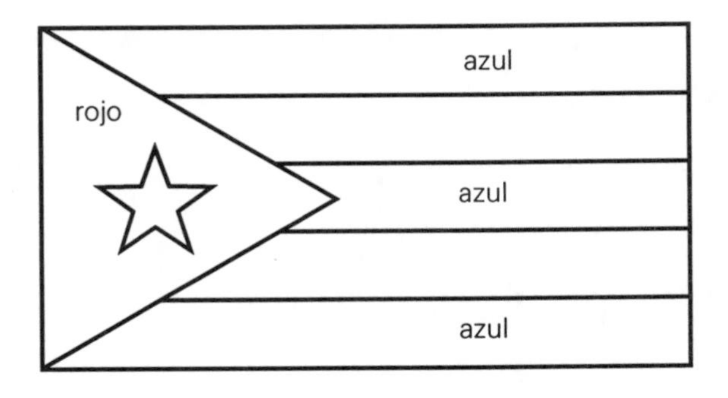

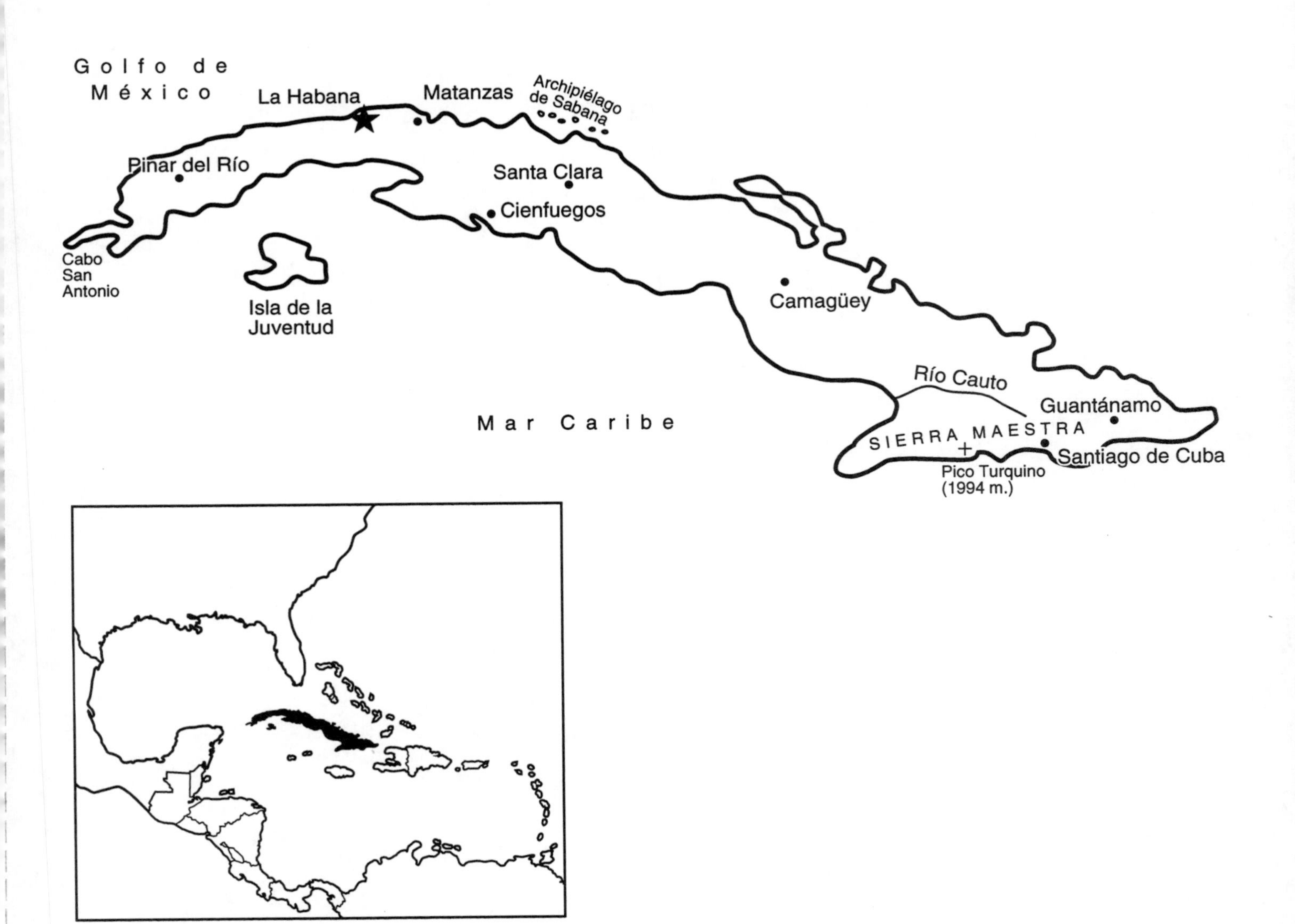

BOLIVIA

Capital: La Paz (Capital oficial: Sucre)
Día de Independencia: 6 de agosto
Habitantes: 7,900,000
Moneda: boliviano

PANAMÁ

Capital: Ciudad de Panamá
Día de Independencia: 3 de noviembre
Habitantes: 2,700,000
Moneda: balboa

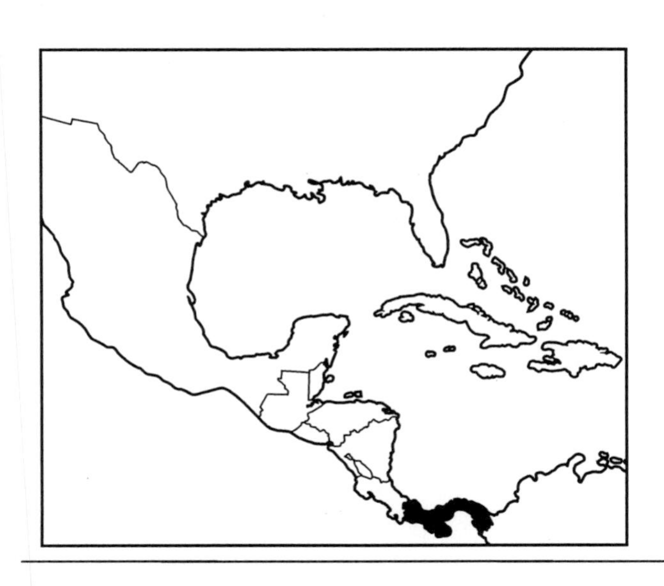

VENEZUELA

Capital: Caracas
Día de Independencia: 5 de julio
Habitantes: 21,000,000
Moneda: bolívar

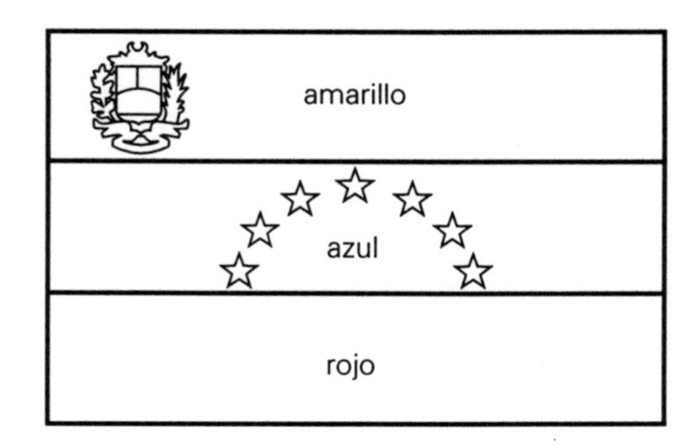

ARGENTINA

Capital: Buenos Aires

Día de Independencia: 9 de julio

Habitantes: 34,300,000

Moneda: peso

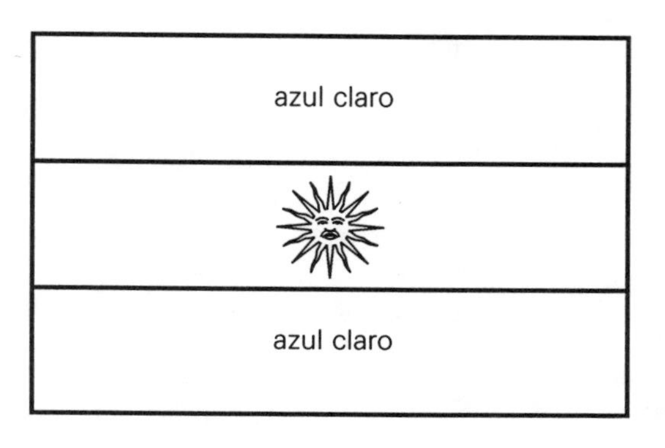